What I See

by Gahan Wilson

Thanks are due the following publications for permission to reprint cartoons that originally appeared in their pages:

Carte Blanche, 33 top, 46 bottom, 111 bottom; *Fantasy & Science Fiction*, 18, 19 top, 21, 24 bottom, 25 bottom, 26, 28 top, 39, 41, 43 top, 57 top, 60 bottom, 76 top, 77, 96 top and bottom, 99, 102 bottom, 110 bottom, 111 top, 116 bottom, 118 top, 120; *Look*, 30 top, 51 top; *The Magazine*, 81 top and bottom, 102 top; *The National Lampoon*, 118 bottom; *The New York Times Book Review*, 38 bottom, 122 bottom; *Playboy*, 7, 12, 16, 23, 27, 35, 37, 40, 47, 50, 55, 56, 59, 64, 68, 71, 74, 78, 83, 84, 86, 90, 95, 100, 103, 107, 109, 113, 117, 123; *Punch*, 67 bottom; *Voices*, 8, 11 bottom, 13, 14 top, 22 bottom, 42 bottom, 75, 88, 121, 122 top, 126.

ISBN 0-671-20858-6
ISBN 0-671-22031-4 pbk.
Library of Congress Catalog Card Number: 75-139667
Manufactured in the United States of America

7   8   9   10

To Whom It May Concern

"I paint what I see, child."

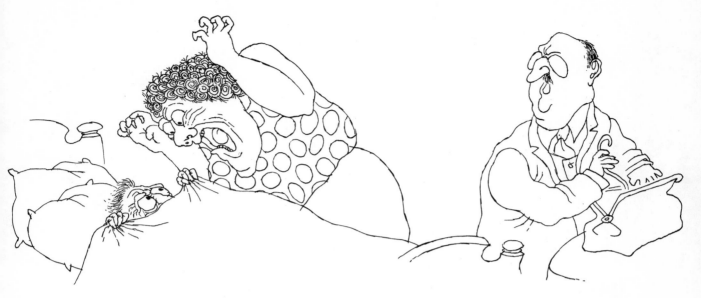

"Oh, yes, and that's another thing, Mrs. Salzman.
Don't do that anymore to Mr. Salzman."

Gahan Wilson

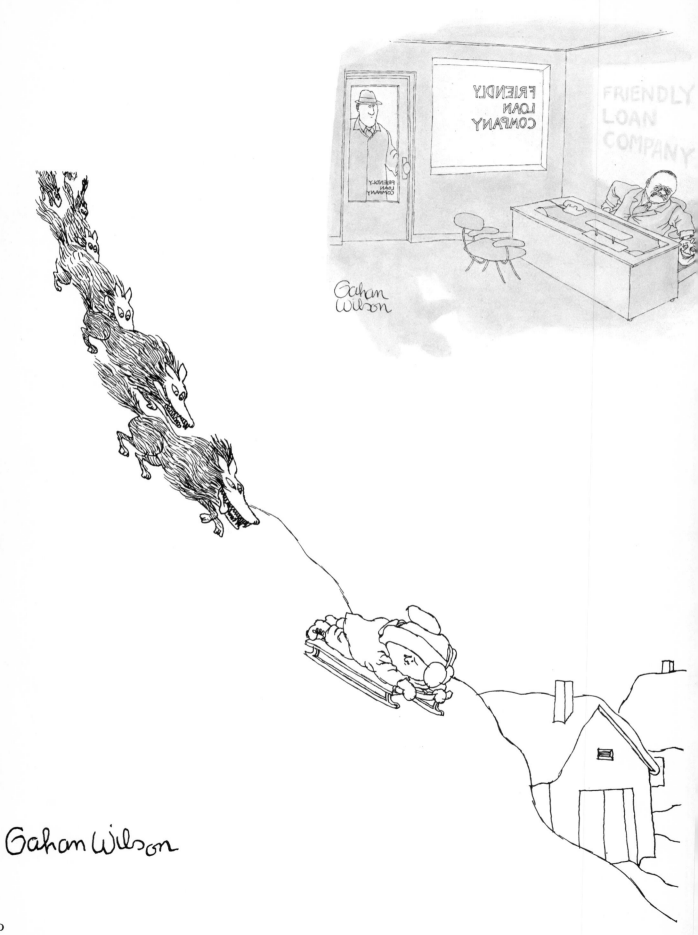

"How many cigarettes a day
have you got it down to, Mr. Leopold?"

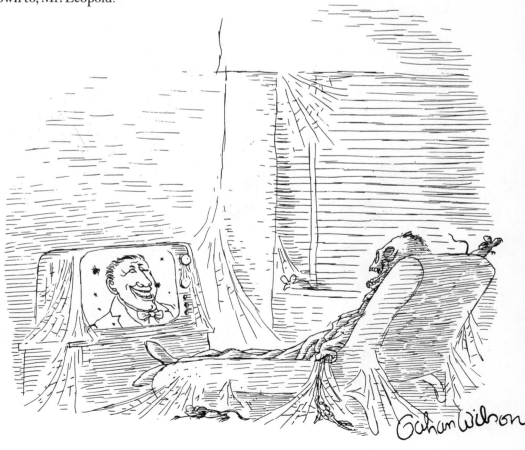

"Hi, gang, glad you dropped by our sprightly nightly,
'cause I think this P.M. we're going to have even more fun than usual!"

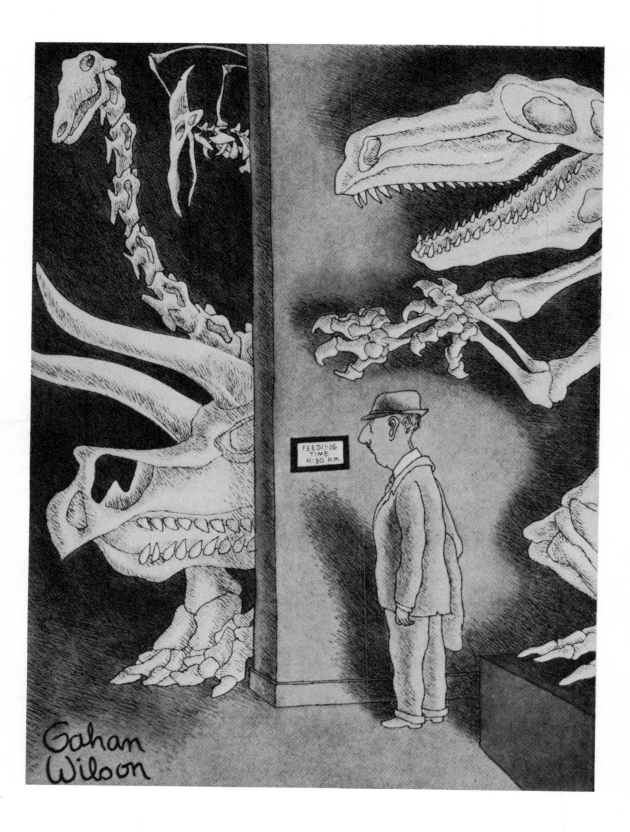

"Don't be afraid, dear—it's a tree!"

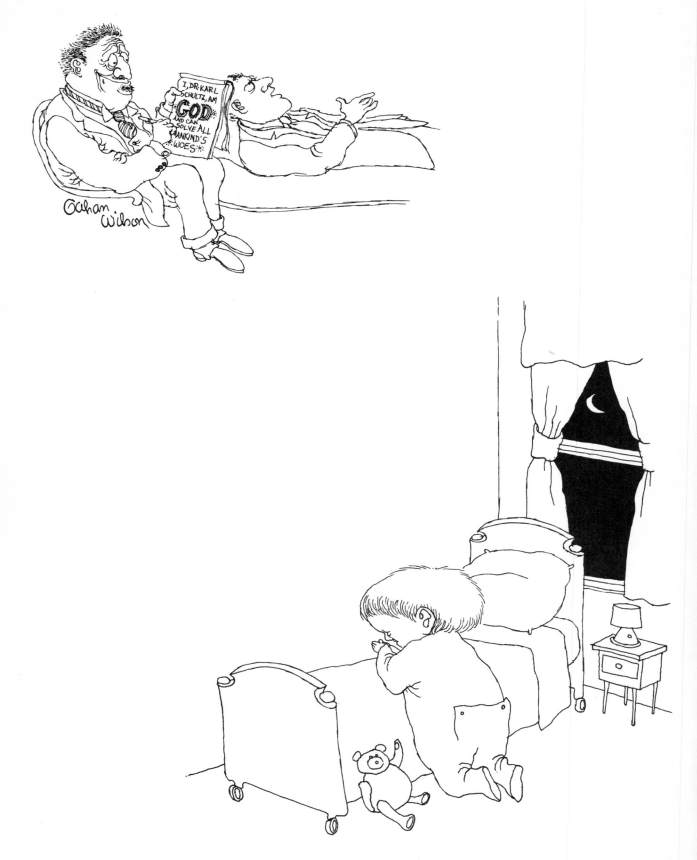

"...And if they won't do it for me then strike them dead with a lightning bolt like you did with Uncle Sherman."

"Big deal!"

"It's the man from the gun lobby, Senator."

"Yes, I'll take this one."

"Well, I guess that pretty well takes care of my anemia diagnosis."

"What's wrong with that damned kid?"

"Yes, it *is* a beautiful view, isn't it?"

"How come we draw all the shaggy dog cases?"

"The set you ordered arrived today, Sir!"

"Where are you *taking* me?"

"Well, that's the story of Little Red
Riding Hood and the Wolf.
Would you like to hear another?"

"In here."

"How much for just the ring?"

"The sandwich-man killer has struck again!"

"Will you shut up with that screaming!"

"Oh, you see both sides to *everything*!"

"Would you like a little something more
to wash that down with?"

"Hey, Mac, which way to the Tall Girls Boutique?"

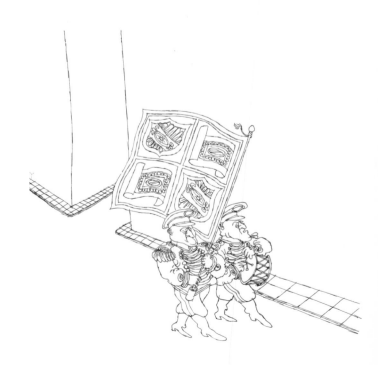

"Let's face it—our parade is a failure!"

"Yeah? Well, they don't make *me* feel
insignificant, fellah!"

"Damned hard luck, Fitzhue."

"How wonderful for her!"

"Well, Sam, Baby, you pulled it off—the biggest deal of them all!"

"The doctors . . . say . . . they've never . . . seen . . . another case quite like it."

"Sure wish we could get us some of that
rain they been having upcountry."

"But, gee whiz, Mr. Baucker, you could at least
let *me* get a little sleep!"

"Well, we found out what's been clogging your chimney since last December, Miss Emmy."

"I've told you to lay off that stuff!"

"No! No! No! No! You haven't got it *cheerful* enough! You haven't got it *light*! I want it *merry*—I want it to *bounce*! Let's take it again from 'Caution: Cigarette smoking may be hazardous...' "

"But surely it must have occurred to you that the wide differences in
your backgrounds would make your marriage more than ordinarily difficult."

39

"It's just as I'd always hoped it would be."

"I only said you could take it with you.
I didn't say you could keep it!"

"That'll be enough of *that*!"

"... A man who George Washington and Abraham Lincoln would be
proud to call 'Mr. President'..."

"Dump all my shares of Peabody and Fenner!"

"I'm far from done, you fool!"

"It's here, again, Henri!"

"So where were you during the tourist season?"

"Today I use my bare hand."

"Another thing—you're going to push the psychedelics
for the syndicate, you got to get
a haircut and a decent suit!"

"Man, it's just like you *said* it would be—totally unspoiled!"

"Get your hands off me, Madame."

"I'm glad we don't draw many like that one!"

"Hey, fellas, wait for me!"

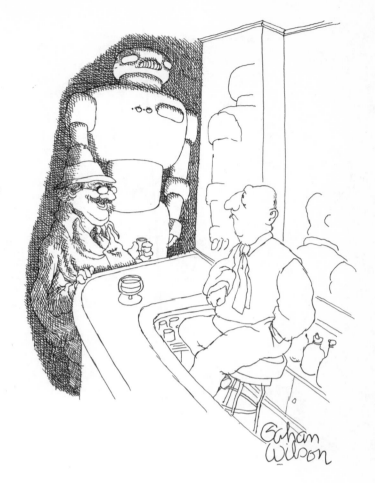

"He's programmed to take me home the minute
I start quoting Nietzsche."

"Something's gone horribly wrong
with the copying machine!"

"It's been awful for business, Mrs. Schultz,
but it was Charlie's last wish."

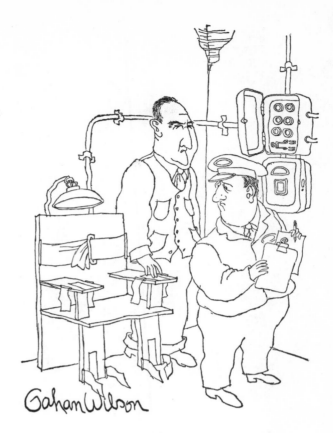

"Your only worry is the bill, Jack."

"See what I mean, Phil? He'd be absolutely perfect
for the lead in that new spy series!"

"You know, you people really have a wonderful sense of rhythm!"

"I'm afraid you have the wrong number."

"No fair turning yourself off, Mr. Hasbrow!"

"When was it you decided to become a bad guy, Ed?"

"Look—I've really *got* to leave!"

"Now exactly at what hour of the evening of December the twenty-fourth did Professor Pohlman query you as to the best method of killing Miss Burkhardt?"

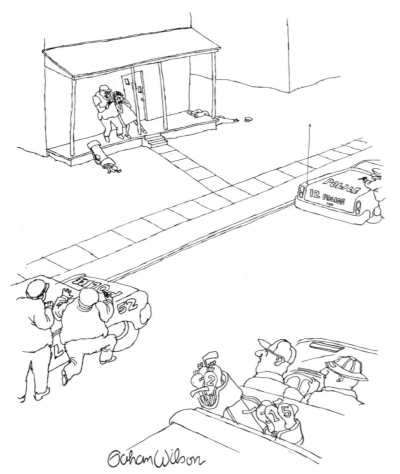

"There goes our threesome!"

"I think you've come down with a bad case of psittacosis."

"I suppose it was bound to happen."

"All right—what's the trouble *this* time?"

"You spit out Dr. Harper this very minute!"

"Listen—can I help it if I look like an elephant?"

"That's what he's smoking, alright!"

"I think it's set to go off around V to IX!"

"There's obviously been some sort of ghastly mistake!"

"Of course if $\int_r^x \nabla^4 \, du = \lim_{n \to \infty} \sum_{i=1}^{n} \left(\frac{1}{n^x}\right)^4 \cdot \frac{x}{n}$, we're sunk."

"*Harvey*! You come down here this *instant*!"

"You come back here, Harry Bartlett!"

"See what I mean? No matter how many times I pull
its trigger, the damned thing just won't fire!"

"... But, seriously ..."

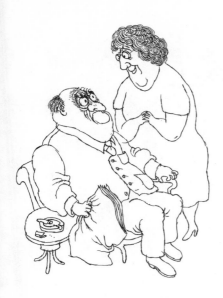

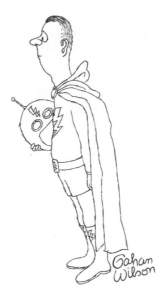

"Now, George, if our Harry wants to dedicate his life
to fighting evildoers and upholding the
forces of law and order, I don't think we
should stand in his way!"

"... And what are you going to do when you grow up?"

"For God's sake—call a policeman!"

"Young man, it's high time you accepted gravity as a fact of life!"

"I just don't understand what's happening
to kids these days!"

"The Boston Strangler!"
"Frankenstein Meets the Wolfman?"
"Breathless?"
"Something by Shakespeare?"

"Harry! *You?*"

"This preparation will eliminate fleas, this one ticks, this one various other vermin and considerable fungi, and this one will eliminate the dog itself."

"There're damned few who can walk away!"

"I'm sorry, young man, I just can't go through
with this ceremony."

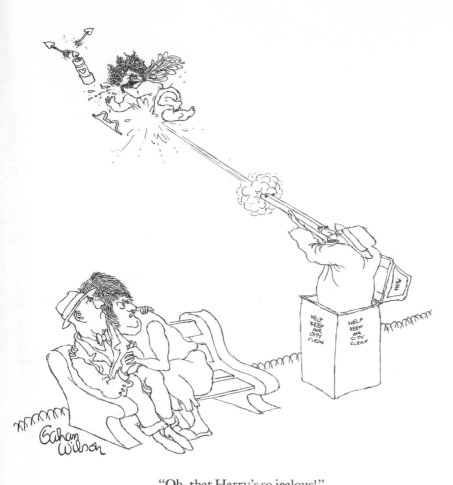

"Oh, that Harry's so jealous!"

"I just love a parade."

"Have fun at the lodge meeting, honey."

"I think I won!"

"You got to hand it to Bloody Eddy—it's the last place
in the world you'd think of as a hideout!"

"...And now for today's international news..."

"Well, I'm sure glad to see you guys don't just arrest *any*body!"

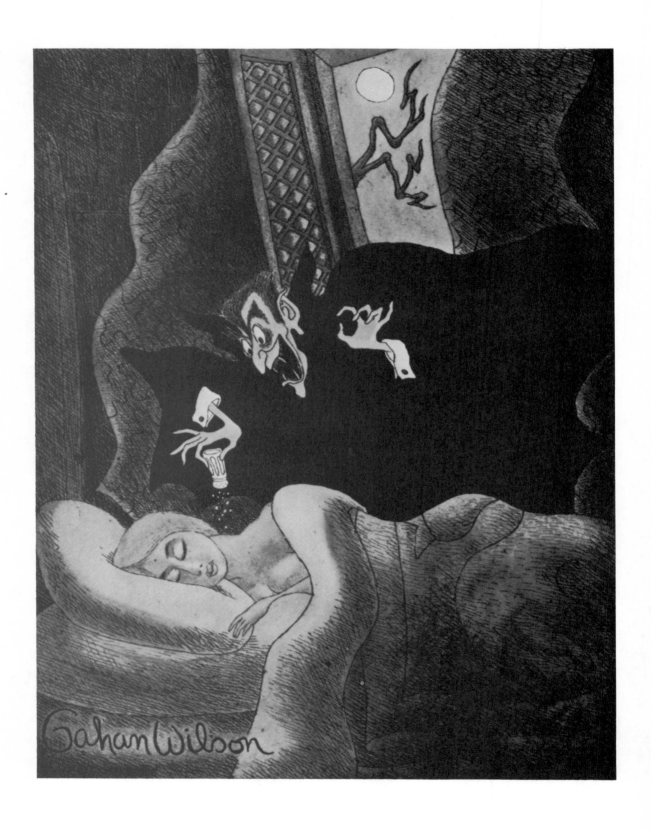

"Thank you. And my friend's is made of rough canvas
and has leather straps sewn into it."

"We'll never get anywhere with these
constant interruptions from the front!"

"This is about that raise, I suppose?"

"... And then, when he was completely satisfied with
the portrait, he pulled the trigger."

"It's a break!"

"You've been letting this boy eat those noisy
breakfast cereals again, haven't you?"

"Alright. Now exhale."

1.

2.

1.

2.

3.

Gahan Wilson

"You're a disgrace to your profession!"

"No, I don't have anything against little, tiny people.
I just don't think you're qualified for the job."

"... Only a minute or so more and man will have his first view
of the other side of the moon!"

"I'm afraid this simulator test indicates Commodore Brent
would be a poor choice for the Lunar Expedition."

"Hold it, Newton. We've been barking up the wrong tree."

"I *thought* I was in particularly good form!"

"What's your frank opinion, Harry?"

"Dinner's ready!"

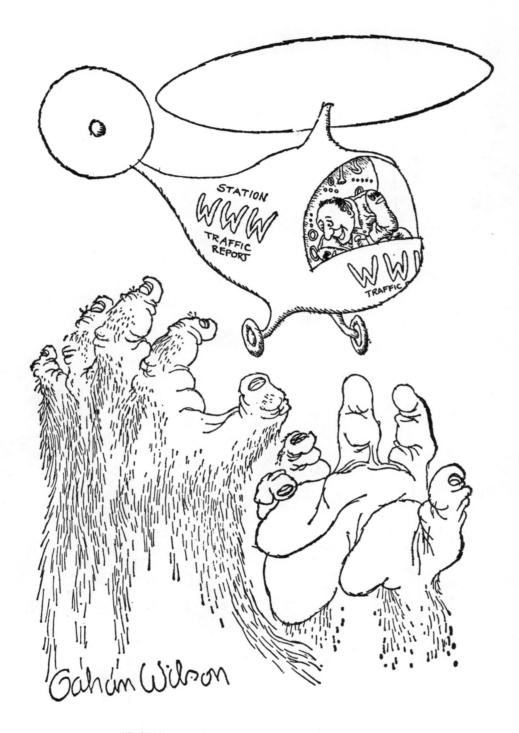

"I think we've located the cause of that tie-up at
Thirty-fourth Street and Seventh Avenue!"

"Thank heaven there are just so many full moons in a year!"

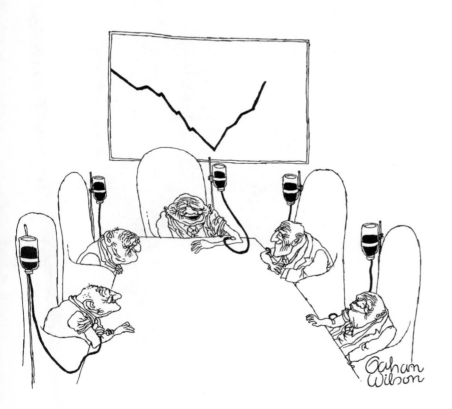

"I've said all along this firm just needed
a little new blood!"

"Poor Fifi hasn't been the same since the veterinarian put
the brain of his hunchbacked assistant into her skull!"

"Och, Sir, my congratulations—'tis a rare stranger
who gets to view the wild haggis romp!"

"Straight ahead, Bernie, dear."

"Mr. Delafield will see you now."

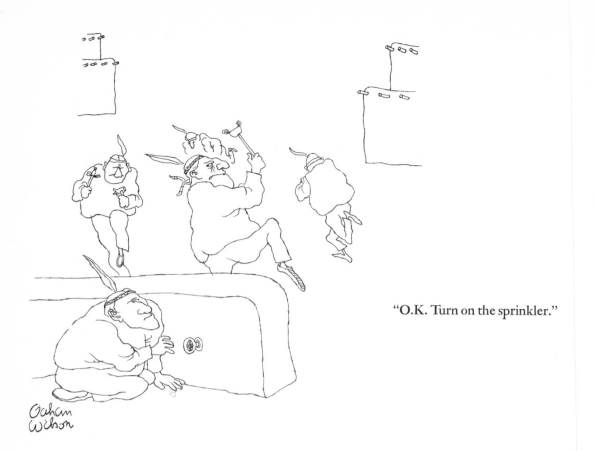

"O.K. Turn on the sprinkler."

"Do you really believe in any of this stuff?"

"Yes, we cater to a rather specialized clientele."

"It isn't easy cutting the heart out of a woman with a dull knife.
And it takes time. It takes a good fifteen minutes."

"What I always say is—*don't get involved!*"

"Better give the missus a touch, too!"

"Now I *know* we're being followed!"

"... And now point out the man you saw murder Miss LaRue!"

"You don't get rid of him that easy, Mrs. Jacowsky."

"For God's sake, Leona, why don't you just finish me off?"

"That one holds Ezra's love letters and this one holds Ezra."

"Oh, go away!"

"It wasn't *always* like this with me . . ."

"Apparently we're not the first one . . ."

Gahan Wilson

"Here she comes again,
and she's got another poodle!"

"I think you would be well advised to locate
the new delphinium bed elsewhere, Hobbs."

"Hey, I'll take some of those!"

"*Now* you got the idea!"

SOON ON THIS SITE
THE
J.B. ROTHMAN
ELEMENTARY
SCHOOL
CONSTRUCTED
FOR THE CITY
BY THE
ACME
CONSTRUCTION
COMPANY

Gahan Wilson

"Oh very well, then—go ahead and set."

"I wish you wouldn't worry so much about me, George.
After all, I'm only a figment of your imagination."

"Good Lord, Holmes! How did you come to know
I'd seafood for lunch?"

123

"Does this mean it's all over between us, Harvey?"

"...and just think—if your ion stabilizer hadn't polarized, we might never have met!"